SIDDUR IN SONG

100 prayerbook melodies

Edited and Arranged
by
VELVEL PASTERNAK

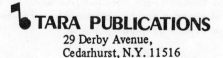
TARA PUBLICATIONS
29 Derby Avenue,
Cedarhurst, N.Y. 11516

ISBN 0-933676-09-3

PRINTED IN THE UNITED STATES

FOREWORD

Although many selections found in "Siddur in Song" have appeared in various Tara Publications editions, the need for a comprehensive volume has long been felt. The editor has not attempted to create an all inclusive edition but rather to make certain portions of the prayer book easier to recite and learn through the vehicle of melody.

In this compilation old traditional tunes appear alongside melodies of the late 20th century. The criterion in the selection of the material has been both singability and the editor's personal tastes.

Please note that a number of songs use the texts as they appear in the Sephardic ritual (*Nusach Sfard*). Also, due to the reverence given to God's name, those songs which repeat His name or are often sung outside synagogue services, such words as *Adonai* and *El* are altered and become *Hashem* and *Kel*.

The editor expresses appreciation to all those composers, both known and unknown, whose melodies fill the pages of this collection.

                                                                V.P.

Contents

KEY TO TRANSLITERATION

a	as in car
ai	as in sigh
e	as in fed
ë	as in they
i	as in pin or me
o	as in form or boat
u	as in true
'	as in it
ch , ḥ	as in Bach

MODE ANI

C. Abramowitz

מוֹדֶה אֲנִי לְפָנֶיךָ, מֶלֶךְ חַי וְקַיָּם
שֶׁהֶחֱזַרְתָּ בִּי נִשְׁמָתִי בְּחֶמְלָה, רַבָּה אֱמוּנָתֶךָ.

Mo-de ani l'fanecha melech chai v'kayam
She-he-che-zarta bi nishmati b'chemla, raba emunatecha.

TORA, TORA

תּוֹרָה צִוָּה לָנוּ מֹשֶׁה
מוֹרָשָׁה קְהִלַּת יַעֲקֹב

Tora tziva lanu Moshe
morasha k'hilat Yaakov

TORA TZIVA

Bostoner Rebbi

Tora to-ra to-ra tzi-va la-nu Mo-she mo-ra-sha k'-hi-lat Ya-a-kov

ra-sha k'-hi-lat Ya-a-kov to-ra to-ra to-ra tzi-va la-nu Mo-she mo-

ra-sha k'-hi-lat Ya-a-kov to-ra to-ra to-ra

tzi-va la-nu Mo-she mo-ra-sha k'-hi-lat Ya-a-kov

תּוֹרָה צִוָּה לָנוּ מֹשֶׁה
מוֹרָשָׁה קְהִלַּת יַעֲקֹב

Tora tziva lanu Moshe
morasha k'hilat Yaakov

SH'MA B'NI

E. Shurin

שְׁמַע בְּנִי מוּסָר אָבִיךְ
וְאַל תִּטֹּשׁ תּוֹרַת אִמֶּךְ

Sh'ma b'ni musar avicha
V'al titosh torat imecha

MA TOVU

מַה טֹּבוּ אֹהָלֶיךָ יַעֲקֹב, מִשְׁכְּנֹתֶיךָ יִשְׂרָאֵל. וַאֲנִי בְּרֹב חַסְדְּךָ אָבוֹא בֵיתֶךָ, אֶשְׁתַּחֲוֶה אֶל הֵיכַל קָדְשְׁךָ בְּיִרְאָתֶךָ. יהוה, אָהַבְתִּי מְעוֹן בֵּיתֶךָ, וּמְקוֹם מִשְׁכַּן כְּבוֹדֶךָ. וַאֲנִי אֶשְׁתַּחֲוֶה וְאֶכְרָעָה, אֶבְרְכָה לִפְנֵי יהוה עֹשִׂי. וַאֲנִי תְפִלָּתִי לְךָ, יהוה, עֵת רָצוֹן. אֱלֹהִים, בְּרָב חַסְדֶּךָ, עֲנֵנִי בֶּאֱמֶת יִשְׁעֶךָ.

Ma tovu ohalecha Ya-akov mishk'no-techa Yisraël
Va-ani b'rov chasd'cha avo vëtecha, eshtacha-ve el
Hëchal kodsh'cha b'yir-atecha, Adonai ahavti m'on
Bëtecha, um'kom mishkan k'vodecha. Va-ani eshta-
chave v'ech-ra-a, evr'cha lif-në Adonai o-si. Va-ani
t'filati l'cha Adonai, ët ratzon. Elohim, b'rav chasdecha, anëni be-emet yish-echa.

ADON OLAM

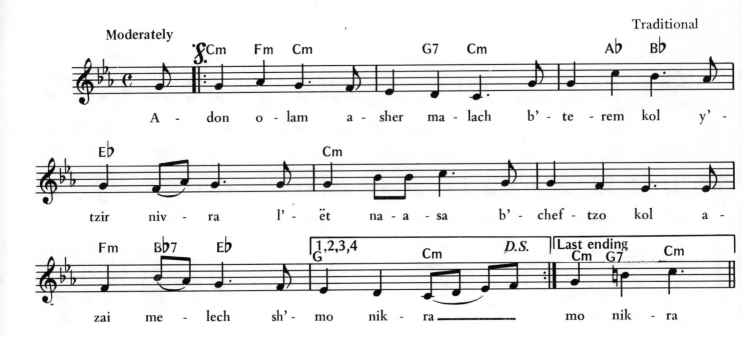

Repeat with additional verses

אֲדוֹן עוֹלָם אֲשֶׁר מָלַךְ   בְּטֶרֶם כָּל־יְצִיר נִבְרָא.
לְעֵת נַעֲשָׂה בְחֶפְצוֹ כֹּל   אֲזַי מֶלֶךְ שְׁמוֹ נִקְרָא.

Adon olam asher malach   b'terem kol y'tzir nivra.
L'ët na-a-sa v'cheftzo kol   azai melech sh'mo nikra.

ADON OLAM No.2

Spritely

Refrain Dm

A - don o-lam a - don o-lam a - sher ma-lach b' - te-rem kol b' te-rem kol y'-

Dm F Gm C7 F

tzir niv - ra l' - ët na - a - sa b' - chef-tzo kol a - zai me-lech____ sh'-

Dm A7 Dm *Verse* F C7

mo nik - ra v' - a - cha - rë kich - lot____ ha-kol l' - va - do yim-loch no -

F Gm Dm F C A7 Dm *Refrain*

ra v' - hu ha - ya v' - hu ho - ve v' - hu yi - ye____ b' - tif - a - ra

Repeat with additional verses

בְּטֶרֶם כָּל־יְצִיר נִבְרָא.   אֲדוֹן עוֹלָם אֲשֶׁר מָלַךְ

אֲזַי מֶלֶךְ שְׁמוֹ נִקְרָא.   לְעֵת נַעֲשָׂה בְחֶפְצוֹ כֹּל

לְבַדּוֹ יִמְלֹךְ נוֹרָא.   וְאַחֲרֵי כִּכְלוֹת הַכֹּל

וְהוּא יִהְיֶה בְּתִפְאָרָה.   וְהוּא הָיָה וְהוּא הֹוֶה

Adon olam asher malach   b'terem kol y'tzir nivra
L'ët na-a-sa b'cheftzo kol   azai melech sh'mo nikra
V'acha-rë kichlot hakol   l'vado yimloch nora
V'hu haya v'hu ho-ve   v'hi yi-ye b'tif-ara

YIGDAL

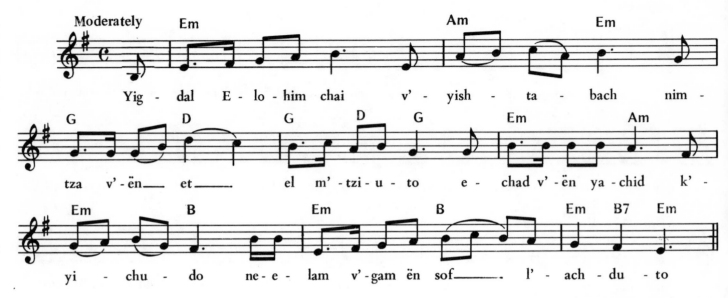

Yig - dal E - lo - him chai v' - yish - ta - bach nim -

tza v' - ën____ et_____ el m'tzi - u - to e - chad v' - ën ya - chid k' -

yi - chu - do ne - e - lam v' - gam ën sof_____ l' - ach - du - to

Repeat with additional verses

נִמְצָא וְאֵין עֵת אֶל מְצִיאוּתוֹ.   יִגְדַּל אֱלֹהִים חַי וְיִשְׁתַּבַּח

נֶעְלָם וְגַם אֵין סוֹף לְאַחְדּוּתוֹ.   אֶחָד וְאֵין יָחִיד כְּיִחוּדוֹ

Yigdal Elohim chai v'yishtabach   nimtza v'ën ët el m'tzi-u-to
Echad v'ën yachid k'yichudo   ne-lam v'gam ën sof l'achduto

YIGDAL No.2

Traditional Portuguese Tune

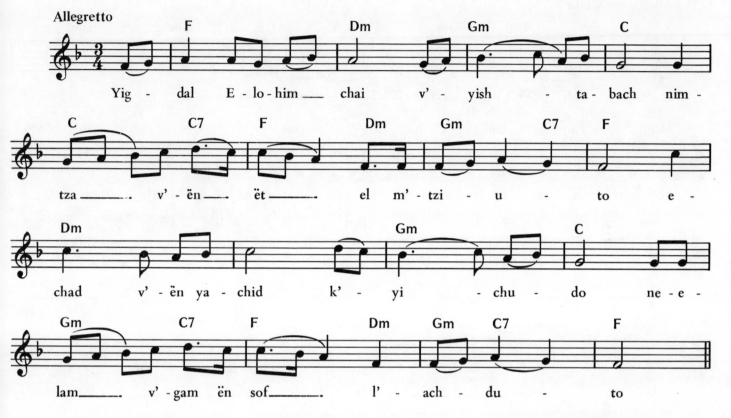

Repeat with additional verses

נִמְצָא וְאֵין עֵת אֶל מְצִיאוּתוֹ.   יִגְדַּל אֱלֹהִים חַי וְיִשְׁתַּבַּח

נֶעְלָם וְגַם אֵין סוֹף לְאַחְדּוּתוֹ.   אֶחָד וְאֵין יָחִיד כְּיִחוּדוֹ

Yigdal Elohim chai v'yishtabach   nimtza v'ën ët el m'tzi-u-to

Echad v'ën yachid k'yi-chu-do   ne-lam v'gam ën sof l'achduto

ASHRENU

אַשְׁרֵינוּ, מַה־טּוֹב חֶלְקֵנוּ וּמַה־נָּעִים גוֹרָלֵנוּ וּמַה יָפָה יְרֻשָּׁתֵנוּ.

Ashrënu ma tov chelkënu uma na-im goralënu uma yafa y'rushatënu

ASHRENU No.2

Hassidic

D.S. al Fine

אַשְׁרֵינוּ, מַה־טוֹב חֶלְקֵנוּ וּמַה־נָּעִים גּוֹרָלֵנוּ וּמַה יָפָה יְרֻשָׁתֵנוּ.

Ashrënu ma tov chelkënu uma na-im goralënu uma yafa y'rushatënu

KEL N'KAMOT HASHEM

Tempo di March

Kël n'-ka-mot Ha-shem Kël n'-ka-mot ho-fi-a hi-na-së sho-fët ha-a-retz ha-shëv g'-mul al gë-im

1. im La-shem hay'-shu-a al__ am-cha bir-cha-te-cha se-
2. la La-shem hay'-shu-a al am-cha vir-cha-te-cha se-la La-shem hay'-shu-a al__ am-cha vir-cha-te-cha se-la la-shem hay'-shu-a al am-cha vir-cha-te-cha se-la

אֵל נְקָמוֹת יהוה, אֵל נְקָמוֹת הוֹפִיעַ.
הִנָּשֵׂא שֹׁפֵט הָאָרֶץ, הָשֵׁב גְּמוּל עַל גֵּאִים.
לַיהוה הַיְשׁוּעָה, עַל עַמְּךָ בִרְכָתֶךָ סֶּלָה.

Kël n'kamot Hashem, Kël n'kamot ho-fi-a.
Hi-na-së shofët ha-a-retz, hashëv g'mul al gë-im.
Lashem hay'shu-a, al amcha vir-cha-techa sela.

HOSHIA ET AMECHA

הוֹשִׁיעָה אֶת־עַמֶּךָ וּבָרֵךְ אֶת־נַחֲלָתֶךָ וּרְעֵם וְנַשְּׂאֵם עַד הָעוֹלָם.

Ho-shi-a et amecha uvarëch et nachalatecha urëm v'nasëm ad ha-olam.

ELECHA

אֵלֶיךָ יהוה אֶקְרָא, וְאֶל אֲדֹנָי אֶתְחַנָּן.
שְׁמַע יהוה וְחָנֵּנִי, יהוה הֱיֵה עֹזֵר לִי.

Ëlecha Hashem ekra, v'el Hashem etchanan.
Sh'ma Hashem v'chanëni, Hashem he-yë ozër li.

IVDU

עִבְדוּ אֶת־יהוה בְּשִׂמְחָה, בֹּאוּ לְפָנָיו בִּרְנָנָה.

Ivdu et Hashem b'simcha, bo-u l'fanav birnana.

RABOT MACHASHAVOT

רַבּוֹת מַחֲשָׁבוֹת בְּלֶב אִישׁ,
וַעֲצַת יהוה הִיא תָקוּם.
עֲצַת יהוה לְעוֹלָם תַּעֲמֹד,
מַחְשְׁבוֹת לִבּוֹ לְדֹר וָדֹר.

Rabot machashavot b'lev ish
Va-a-tzat Hashem hi takum
Atzat Hashem l'olam ta-amod
Mach-sh'vot libo l'dor vador.

ASHRE

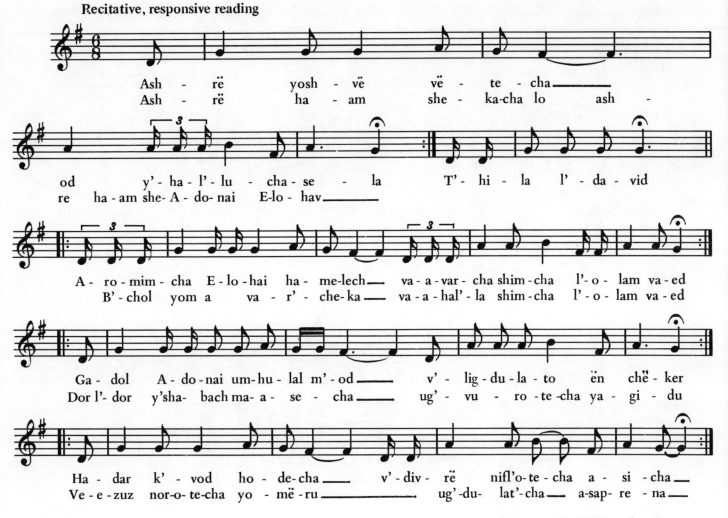

Recitative, responsive reading

Repeat with additional verses

אַשְׁרֵי יוֹשְׁבֵי בֵיתֶךָ, עוֹד יְהַלְלוּךָ סֶּלָה.

אַשְׁרֵי הָעָם שֶׁכָּכָה לֹו, אַשְׁרֵי הָעָם שֶׁיהוה אֱלֹהָיו.

תְּהִלָּה לְדָוִד

אֲרוֹמִמְךָ אֱלוֹהַי הַמֶּלֶךְ, וַאֲבָרְכָה שִׁמְךָ לְעוֹלָם וָעֶד.

בְּכָל־יוֹם אֲבָרְכֶךָּ, וַאֲהַלְלָה שִׁמְךָ לְעוֹלָם וָעֶד.

גָּדוֹל יהוה וּמְהֻלָּל מְאֹד, וְלִגְדֻלָּתוֹ אֵין חֵקֶר.

דּוֹר לְדוֹר יְשַׁבַּח מַעֲשֶׂיךָ, וּגְבוּרֹתֶיךָ יַגִּידוּ.

הֲדַר כְּבוֹד הוֹדֶךָ, וְדִבְרֵי נִפְלְאֹתֶיךָ אָשִׂיחָה.

וֶעֱזוּז נוֹרְאֹתֶיךָ יֹאמֵרוּ, וּגְדֻלָּתְךָ אֲסַפְּרֶנָּה.

Ashrë yoshvë vëtecha, od y'hal'lucha sela
Ashrë ha-am shekacha lo, ashrë ha-am she-Adonai Elohav.
T'hila l'David
Aromimcha Elohai hamelech, va-avarcha shimcha l'olam va-ed.
B'chol yom avarcheka, va-a-hal'la shimcha l'olam va-ed.
Gadol Adonai um'hulal m'od, v'ligdulato ën chëker.
Dor L'dor y'shabach ma-a-secha, ugvurotecha yagidu.
Hadar k'vod ho-decha, v'divrë nifl'otecha asicha.
Ve-e-zuz no-r'-otecha yo-më-ru ug-dulatcha asaprena.

MALCHUTCHA

R. Sirotkin

מַלְכוּתְךָ מַלְכוּת כָּל־עֹלָמִים, וּמֶמְשַׁלְתְּךָ בְּכָל־דּוֹר וָדֹר.

Malchutcha malchut kol olamim, umemshalt'cha b'chol dor vador

SHAB'CHI

S. Rockoff

שַׁבְּחִי יְרוּשָׁלַיִם אֶת־יהוה, הַלְלִי אֱלֹקַיִךְ צִיּוֹן.

Shab'chi Y'rushalayim et Hashem, hal'li Elokayich Tziyon.

KI LASHEM HAMLUCHA

Allegro moderato

Ki la - shem___ ha - m'- lu - cha u - mo - shël
ba - go - yim u - mo - shël ba - go - yim ki la - shem
ha - m'- lu - cha u - mo - shël ba - go - yim

כִּי לַיהוה הַמְּלוּכָה וּמוֹשֵׁל בַּגוֹיִם.

Ki Lashem ham'lucha umoshël bagoyim.

BARCHU

בָּרְכוּ אֶת־יהוה הַמְבֹרָךְ.
בָּרוּךְ יהוה הַמְבֹרָךְ לְעוֹלָם וָעֶד.

Barchu et Adonai hamvorach
Baruch Adonai hamvorach l'olam va-ed.

V'CHULAM M'KABLIM

וְכֻלָּם מְקַבְּלִים עֲלֵיהֶם עַל מַלְכוּת שָׁמַיִם זֶה מִזֶּה

V'chulam m'kablim alëhem ol malchut shamayim ze mi-ze

AVINU HA-AV HARACHAMAN

אָבִינוּ הָאָב הָרַחֲמָן, הַמְרַחֵם, רַחֵם עָלֵינוּ
וְתֵן בְּלִבֵּנוּ לְהָבִין וּלְהַשְׂכִּיל, לִשְׁמֹעַ,
לִלְמֹד וּלְלַמֵּד, לִשְׁמֹר וְלַעֲשׂוֹת וּלְקַיֵּם

Avinu ha-av harachaman, ham'rachëm, rachëm alënu
V'tën b'libënu l'havin ul'haskil, lishmo-a
Lilmod ul'lamëd, lishmor v'la-a-sot ul'kayëm

V'HAER ENENU

S. Carlebach

V'ha-ër ënënu b'toratecha, v'dabëk libënu b'mitzvotecha,
V'yachëd l'vavënu l'ahava ul'yira et sh'mecha.
V'lo nëvosh v'lo nikalëm v'lo nikashël, l'olam va-ed.

*וְהָאֵר עֵינֵינוּ בְּתוֹרָתֶךָ
וְדַבֵּק לִבֵּנוּ בְּמִצְוֹתֶיךָ
וְיַחֵד לְבָבֵנוּ
לְאַהֲבָה וּלְיִרְאָה אֶת שְׁמֶךָ
וְלֹא נֵבוֹשׁ וְלֹא נִכָּלֵם
וְלֹא נִכָּשֵׁל לְעוֹלָם וָעֶד

*Text as found in the Nusach S'phard prayerbook

EMET

אֱמֶת אַתָּה הוּא רִאשׁוֹן וְאַתָּה הוּא אַחֲרוֹן,
וּמִבַּלְעָדֶיךָ אֵין לָנוּ מֶלֶךְ גּוֹאֵל וּמוֹשִׁיעַ.

Emet ata hu rishon v'ata hu acharon
Umibaladecha ën lanu melech go-ël umoshia.

M'CHALKEL CHAYIM

מְכַלְכֵּל חַיִּים בְּחֶסֶד, מְחַיֶּה מֵתִים בְּרַחֲמִים רַבִּים, סוֹמֵךְ
נוֹפְלִים וְרוֹפֵא חוֹלִים וּמַתִּיר אֲסוּרִים, וּמְקַיֵּם אֱמוּנָתוֹ לִישֵׁנֵי
עָפָר. מִי כָמוֹךָ בַּעַל גְּבוּרוֹת וּמִי דּוֹמֶה לָּךְ, מֶלֶךְ מֵמִית וּמְחַיֶּה
וּמַצְמִיחַ יְשׁוּעָה.

M'chalkël chayim b'chesed, m'chayë mëtim b'rachamim rabim, somëch
Noflim v'ro-fë cholim umatir asurim, um'ka-yëm emunato lishë-në afar.
Mi chamocha ba-al g'vu-rot umi do-me lach, melech mëmit um'cha-ye
Umatz-mi-ach y'shu-a.

V'TECHEZENA

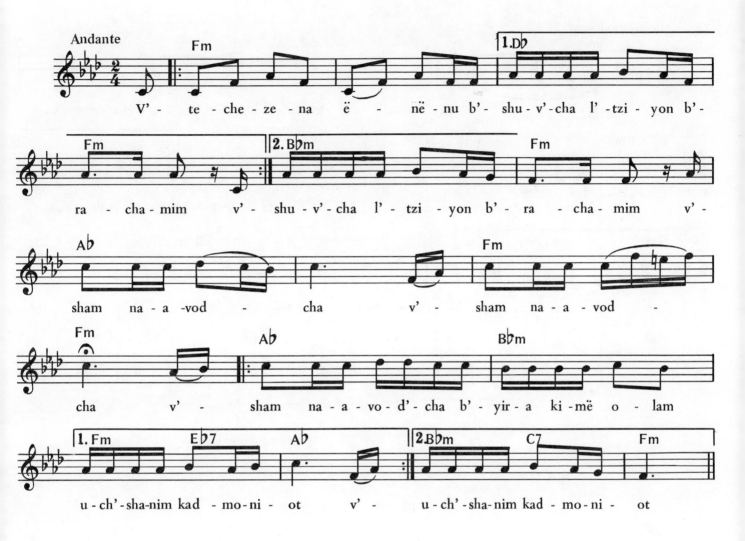

V'-te-che-ze-na ënë-nu b'-shu-v'-cha l'-tzi-yon b'-ra-cha-mim v'-shu-v'-cha l'-tzi-yon b'-ra-cha-mim v'-sham na-a-vod-cha v'-sham na-a-vod-cha v'-sham na-a-vo-d'-cha b'-yir-a ki-më o-lam u-ch'-sha-nim kad-mo-ni-ot v'-u-ch'-sha-nim kad-mo-ni-ot

וְתֶחֱזֶינָה עֵינֵינוּ בְּשׁוּבְךָ לְצִיּוֹן בְּרַחֲמִים.

V'techezena ënënu b'shuv'cha l'tziyon b'rachamim

HATOV

הַטּוֹב כִּי לֹא כָלוּ רַחֲמֶיךָ,
וְהַמְרַחֵם כִּי לֹא תַמּוּ חֲסָדֶיךָ,
כִּי מֵעוֹלָם קִוִּינוּ לָךְ.

Hatov ki lo chalu rachamecha,
V'ham'rachëm ki lo tamu cha-sa-decha,
Ki më-olam kivinu lach.

AL HANISIM

עַל הַנִּסִּים וְעַל הַפֻּרְקָן, וְעַל הַגְּבוּרוֹת, וְעַל הַתְּשׁוּעוֹת, וְעַל הַמִּלְחָמוֹת שֶׁעָשִׂיתָ לַאֲבוֹתֵינוּ בַּיָּמִים הָהֵם בַּזְּמַן הַזֶּה.

Al hanisim v'al hapurkan v'al hagvurot, v'al hatshuot v'al
Hamilchamot she-a-sita la-avotënu bayamim hahëm bazman ha-ze.

AL HANISIM No.2

עַל הַנִּסִּים וְעַל הַפֻּרְקָן, וְעַל הַגְּבוּרוֹת, וְעַל הַתְּשׁוּעוֹת, וְעַל
הַמִּלְחָמוֹת שֶׁעָשִׂיתָ לַאֲבוֹתֵינוּ בַּיָּמִים הָהֵם בַּזְּמַן הַזֶּה.

Al hanisim v'al hapurkan v'al hagvurot, v'al hatshu-ot v'al
Hamilchamot she-a-sita la-avotënu bayamim hahëm bazman ha-ze.

BARCHENU

Moderately with feeling

S. Carlebach

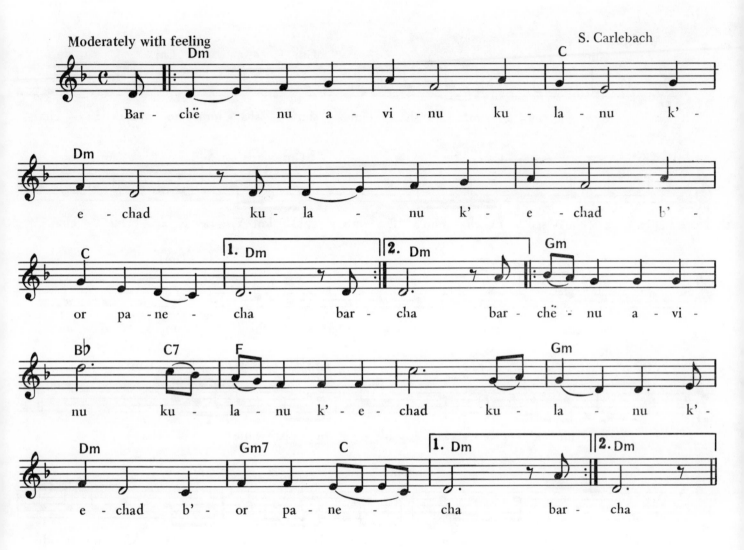

Bar - chë - nu a - vi - nu ku - la - nu k' - e - chad ku - la - nu k' - e - chad b' - or pa - ne - cha bar - cha bar - chë - nu a - vi - nu ku - la - nu k' - e - chad ku - la - nu k' - e - chad b' - or pa - ne - cha bar - cha

בָּרְכֵנוּ אָבִינוּ כֻּלָּנוּ כְּאֶחָד בְּאוֹר פָּנֶיךָ

Barchënu avinu kulanu k'echad b'or panecha

SIM SHALOM

שִׂים שָׁלוֹם טוֹבָה וּבְרָכָה, חֵן נָחֶסֶד וְרַחֲמִים עָלֵינוּ
וְעַל כָּל־יִשְׂרָאֵל עַמֶּךְ. בָּרְכֵנוּ אָבִינוּ כֻּלָנוּ כְּאֶחָד בְּאוֹר פָּנֶיךָ,
כִּי בְאוֹר פָּנֶיךָ נָתַתָּ לָנוּ, יהוה אֱלֹהֵינוּ, תּוֹרַת חַיִּים וְאַהֲבַת
חֶסֶד, וּצְדָקָה וּבְרָכָה וְרַחֲמִים וְחַיִּים וְשָׁלוֹם.

Sim shalom tova uvracha, chën va-chesed v'rachamim alënu
V'al kol Yisraël amecha. Barchënu avinu kulanu k'echad b'or panecha,
Ki v'or panecha natata lanu, Adonai Elohënu, torat chayim v'ahavat
Chesed, utzdaka uvracha v'rachamim v'chayim v'shalom.

SHALOM RAV

שָׁלוֹם רָב עַל יִשְׂרָאֵל עַמְּךָ תָּשִׂים לְעוֹלָם,
כִּי אַתָּה הוּא מֶלֶךְ אָדוֹן לְכָל־הַשָּׁלוֹם. וְטוֹב בְּעֵינֶיךָ לְבָרֵךְ
אֶת־עַמְּךָ יִשְׂרָאֵל בְּכָל־עֵת וּבְכָל־שָׁעָה בִּשְׁלוֹמֶךָ.

Shalom rav al Yisraël amcha tasim l'olam,
Ki ata hu melech adon l'chol hashalom. V'tov b'ënecha
L'varëch et amcha Yisraël b'chol ët uv'chol sha-a bishlomecha.

OSE SHALOM

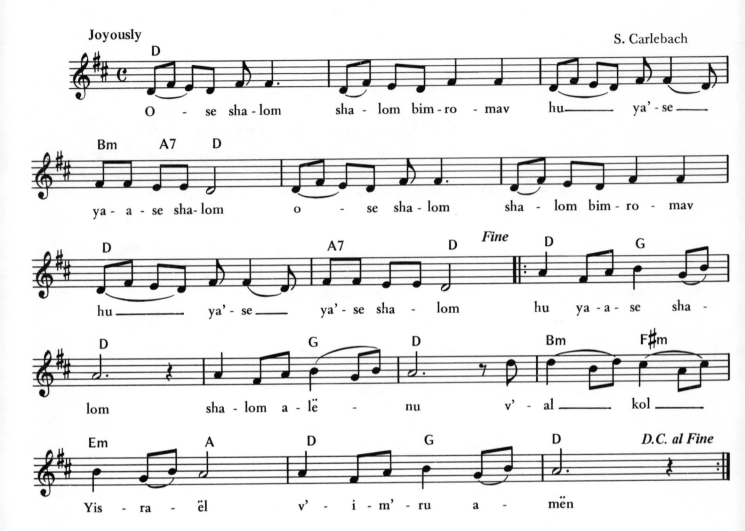

עוֹשֶׂה שָׁלוֹם בִּמְרוֹמָיו, הוּא בְּרַחֲמָיו יַעֲשֶׂה שָׁלוֹם עָלֵינוּ וְעַל
כָּל־יִשְׂרָאֵל, וְאִמְרוּ אָמֵן.

O-se shalom bimromav hu ya-a-se shalom alënu v'al
Kol Yisraël, v'imru Amën.

SHEYIBANE BET HAMIKDASH

I. Schor

שֶׁיִּבָּנֶה בֵּית הַמִּקְדָּשׁ
בִּמְהֵרָה בְיָמֵנוּ
וְתֵן חֶלְקֵנוּ בְּתוֹרָתֶךְ

Sheyiba-ne bët hamikdash
Bimhëra v'yamënu
V'tën chelkënu b'toratecha

AVINU MALKENU

Traditional

אָבִינוּ מַלְכֵּנוּ, חָנֵּנוּ וַעֲנֵנוּ, כִּי אֵין בָּנוּ מַעֲשִׂים,
עֲשֵׂה עִמָּנוּ צְדָקָה וָחֶסֶד וְהוֹשִׁיעֵנוּ.

Avinu malkënu, chanënu va-anënu, ki ën banu ma-asim.
A-së imanu tz'daka vachesed v'ho-shi-ënu.

HASHEM ELOKE YISRAEL

Y. Weinreb

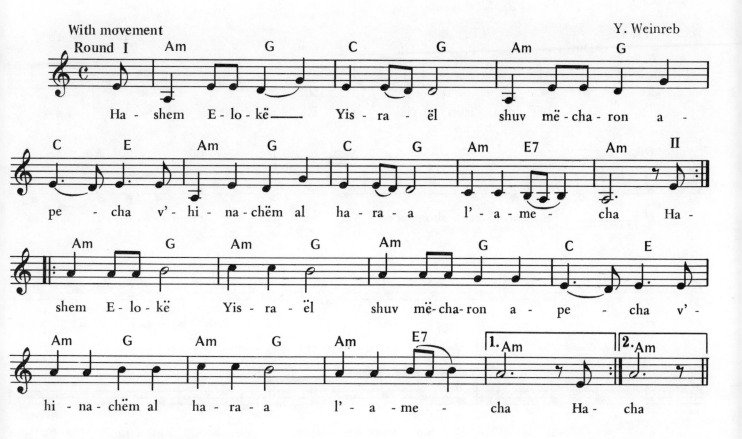

יהוה אֱלֹהֵי יִשְׂרָאֵל, שׁוּב מֵחֲרוֹן אַפֶּךָ וְהִנָּחֵם עַל הָרָעָה לְעַמֶּךָ.

Hashem Elokë Yisraël shuv më-charon apecha
V'hinachëm al ha-ra-a l'amecha.

SHOMER YISRAEL

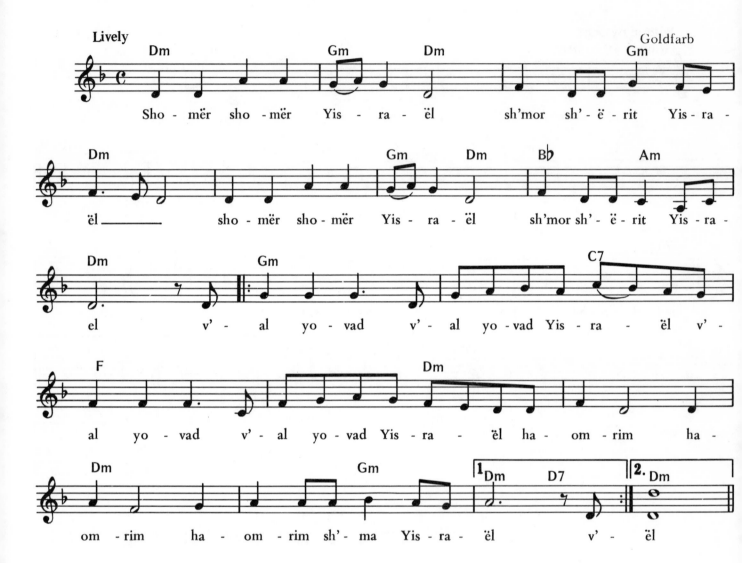

שׁוֹמֵר יִשְׂרָאֵל, שְׁמוֹר שְׁאֵרִית יִשְׂרָאֵל,
וְאַל יֹאבַד יִשְׂרָאֵל, הָאֹמְרִים שְׁמַע יִשְׂרָאֵל.

Shomër Yisraël, sh'mor sh'ërit Yisraël,
V'al yovad Yisraël, ha-omrim sh'ma Yisraël.

BARUCH ELOHENU

Ba - ruch E - lo - hё - nu she - bra - a - nu lich - vo - do

v' - hiv - di - la - nu min ha - to - im v' - na - tan la - nu to - rat e -

met   met   ba - ruch E - lo - hё - nu she - bra -

a - nu lich - vo - do   v' - hiv - di - la - nu

min ha - to - im v' - na - tan la - nu to - rat e - met   met

בָּרוּךְ אֱלֹהֵינוּ שֶׁבְּרָאָנוּ לִכְבוֹדוֹ, וְהִבְדִּילָנוּ מִן הַתּוֹעִים,
וְנָתַן לָנוּ תּוֹרַת אֱמֶת

Baruch Elohёnu sheb-ra-anu lichvodo, v'hivdilanu min hato-im,
V'natan lanu torat emet

AL TIRA

S. Carlebach

אַל תִּירָא מִפַּחַד פִּתְאֹם, וּמִשֹּׁאַת רְשָׁעִים כִּי תָבֹא. עֵצוּ עֵצָה
וְתֻפָר, דַּבְּרוּ דָבָר וְלֹא יָקוּם, כִּי עִמָּנוּ אֵל.

Al tira mipachad pitom, umi-sho-at r'sha-im ki tavo. Utzu ëtza
V'tufar dabru davar v'lo yakum, ki imanu El.

S'U SH'ARIM

שְׂאוּ שְׁעָרִים רָאשֵׁיכֶם,
וְהִנָּשְׂאוּ פִּתְחֵי עוֹלָם,
וְיָבוֹא מֶלֶךְ הַכָּבוֹד.

S'u sh'arim roshĕchem,
V'hi-nas'u pit-chĕ o-lam,
V'yavo melech hakavod.

ACHAT SHA-ALTI

אַחַת שָׁאַלְתִּי מֵאֵת יהוה, אוֹתָהּ אֲבַקֵּשׁ:
שִׁבְתִּי בְּבֵית יהוה כָּל־יְמֵי חַיַּי,
לַחֲזוֹת בְּנֹעַם יהוה וּלְבַקֵּר בְּהֵיכָלוֹ.

Achat sha-alti më-ët Hashem. o-ta a-va-kësh:
Shivti b'vët Hashem kol y'më chayai,
Lachazot b'no-am Hashem ul'vakër b'hëchalo.

HORENI HASHEM

With feeling

Y. Begun

Horëni Hashem darkecha un'chëni b'orach mishor l'ma-an shor'rai.
Lu-lë he-emanti lirot b'tuv Hashem b'eretz chayim.

הוֹרֵנִי יהוה דַּרְכֶּךָ וּנְחֵנִי בְּאֹרַח מִישׁוֹר לְמַעַן שׁוֹרְרָי.
לוּלֵא הֶאֱמַנְתִּי לִרְאוֹת בְּטוּב יהוה בְּאֶרֶץ חַיִּים.

ANI MA-AMIN

Moderately

M. Parnes

A - ni ma - a - min _____ be - e - mu - na sh' - lë -

ma _____ b' - vi - at ha - ma - shi - ach a - ni

1. ma - a - min _____ 2. ma - min _____ v' -

af al pi she - yit - ma - më - a im kol ze a -

cha - ke lo _____ a - cha - ke lo b' - chol yom she -

ya - vo b' - chol yom she - ya - vo _____

אֲנִי מַאֲמִין בֶּאֱמוּנָה שְׁלֵמָה בְּבִיאַת הַמָּשִׁיחַ
וְאַף עַל פִּי שֶׁיִּתְמַהְמֵהַּ עִם כָּל זֶה
אֲחַכֶּה לּוֹ בְּכָל יוֹם שֶׁיָּבוֹא

Ani ma-amin be-emuna sh'lëma b'vi-at ha-ma-shi-ach
V'af al pi she-yit-ma-më-a im kol ze acha-ke lo b'chol
Yom she-ya-vo.

ACHAKE LO

וְאַף עַל פִּי שֶׁיִּתְמַהְמֵהַּ עִם כָּל זֶה
אֲחַכֶּה לוֹ בְּכָל יוֹם שֶׁיָבוֹא

V'af al pi she-yit-ma-më-a im kol ze
acha-ke lo b'chol Yom she-ya-vo.

YISM'CHU HASHAMAYIM

Hassidic

Yis - m' - chu ha - sha - ma - yim   yis - m' - chu ha - sha - ma - yim

yis - m' - chu ha - sha - ma - yim___ v' - ta - gël___ ha - a - retz   retz

yir - am ha - yam   yir - am ha - yam   yir - am ha - yam___ u - m' - lo - o   lo - o

yir - am ha - yam   yir - am ha - yam   yir - am ha - yam___ u - m' - lo - o   lo - o___

יִשְׂמְחוּ הַשָּׁמַיִם וְתָגֵל הָאָרֶץ,
יִרְעַם הַיָּם וּמְלֹאוֹ.

Yism'chu hashamayim v'tagël ha-aretz.
Yiram hayam um'lo-o.

ROM'MU

רוֹמְמוּ יהוה אֱלֹהֵינוּ
וְהִשְׁתַּחֲווּ לְהַר קָדְשׁוֹ

Rom'mu Hashem Elokënu
V'hishtachavu l'har kodsho

MIZMOR L'DAVID

D.S. al Fine

uv'-hĕ-cha-lo_____ ku- lo_____ o-mĕr___ ka-vod

מִזְמוֹר לְדָוִד.
הָבוּ לַיהוה, בְּנֵי אֵלִים, הָבוּ לַיהוה כָּבוֹד וָעֹז.
הָבוּ לַיהוה כְּבוֹד שְׁמוֹ, הִשְׁתַּחֲווּ לַיהוה בְּהַדְרַת קֹדֶשׁ.
קוֹל יהוה עַל הַמָּיִם, אֵל הַכָּבוֹד הִרְעִים,
יהוה עַל מַיִם רַבִּים.
קוֹל יהוה בַּכֹּחַ, קוֹל יהוה בֶּהָדָר.

קוֹל יהוה שֹׁבֵר אֲרָזִים וַיְשַׁבֵּר יהוה אֶת־אַרְזֵי הַלְּבָנוֹן.
וַיַּרְקִידֵם כְּמוֹ עֵגֶל, לְבָנוֹן וְשִׂרְיוֹן כְּמוֹ בֶן־רְאֵמִים.
קוֹל יהוה חֹצֵב לַהֲבוֹת אֵשׁ.
קוֹל יהוה יָחִיל מִדְבָּר, יָחִיל יהוה מִדְבַּר קָדֵשׁ.
קוֹל יהוה יְחוֹלֵל אַיָּלוֹת
וַיֶּחֱשֹׂף יְעָרוֹת, וּבְהֵיכָלוֹ כֻּלּוֹ אֹמֵר כָּבוֹד.
יהוה לַמַּבּוּל יָשָׁב, וַיֵּשֶׁב יהוה מֶלֶךְ לְעוֹלָם.
יהוה עֹז לְעַמּוֹ יִתֵּן, יהוה יְבָרֵךְ אֶת־עַמּוֹ בַשָּׁלוֹם.

Mizmor L'david.
Havu Ladonai, b'nĕ elim, havu Ladonai kavod va-oz.
Havu ladonai k'vod sh'mo, hishtachavu Ladonai b'hadrat kodesh.
Kol Adonai al hamayim, El hakavod hirim
Adonai al mayim rabim.
Kol Adonai ba-ko-ach, kol Adonai be-hadar.

Kol Adonai shovĕr arazim vay'shabĕr Adonai et arzĕ halvanon.
Vayar-kidĕm k'mo ĕgel, l'vanon v'siryon k'mo ven r'ĕmim.
Kol Adonai chotzĕv lahavot ĕsh.
Kol Adonai yachil midbar, yachil Adonai midbar kadĕsh.
Kol Adonai y'cholĕl ayalot
Vayechesof y'arot, uv'hĕ-chalo kulo omĕr kavod.
Adonai lamabul yashav, vayĕshev Adonai melech l'olam.
Adonai oz l'amo yitĕn, Adonai y'varĕch et amo vashalom.

L'CHA DODI

Repeat with additional verses

לְכָה דוֹדִי לִקְרַאת כַּלָה, פְּנֵי שַׁבָּת נְקַבְּלָה.

שָׁמוֹר וְזָכוֹר בְּדִבּוּר אֶחָד

הִשְׁמִיעָנוּ אֵל הַמְיוּחָד.

יהוה אֶחָד וּשְׁמוֹ אֶחָד

לְשֵׁם וּלְתִפְאֶרֶת וְלִתְהִלָה.

L'cha dodi likrat kala, p'në Shabat n'kab'la.

Shamor v'zachor b'dibur echad
Hishmi-anu Ël hamyuchad
Adonai echad ush'mo echad
L'shëm ul-tif-eret v'lithila.

TOV L'HODOT

Tempo di Valse   I. Katz

Tov l'-ho-dot ___ l'-ho - dot la-shem ___

u - - l'-za - mër l'-shim-cha el-yon ___

yon ___ l'-ha - gid ba-bo-ker chas-de-cha ve-mu-nat-cha

ba-lë-lot l'-ha - gid ba-bo-ker chas-de-cha

ve-mu-nat - cha ba - lë-lot l'-lot

טוֹב לְהֹדוֹת לַיהוָה, וּלְזַמֵּר לְשִׁמְךָ עֶלְיוֹן.
לְהַגִּיד בַּבֹּקֶר חַסְדֶּךָ, וֶאֱמוּנָתְךָ בַּלֵּילוֹת.

Tov l'hodot Lashem, ul'zamër l'shimcha Elyon.
L'hagid baboker chasdecha, ve-emunatcha ba-lëlot.

TOV L'HODOT No.2

Allegro moderato

S. Carlebach

טוֹב לְהֹדוֹת לַיהוה, וּלְזַמֵּר לְשִׁמְךָ עֶלְיוֹן.

Tov l'hodot Lashem, ul'zamër l'shimcha elyon.

TZADIK KATAMAR

צַדִּיק כַּתָּמָר יִפְרָח,
כְּאֶרֶז בַּלְּבָנוֹן יִשְׂגֶּה.
שְׁתוּלִים בְּבֵית יהוה,
בְּחַצְרוֹת אֱלֹהֵינוּ יַפְרִיחוּ.
עוֹד יְנוּבוּן בְּשֵׂיבָה, דְּשֵׁנִים וְרַעֲנַנִּים יִהְיוּ.
לְהַגִּיד כִּי יָשָׁר יהוה, צוּרִי וְלֹא עַוְלָתָה בּוֹ.

Tzadik katamar yifrach,
K'erez balvanon yis-ge
Sh'tulim b'vët Adonai
B'chatzrot Elohënu yafrichu
Od y'nuvun b'së-va d'shēnim v'ra-ananim yiyu
L'hagid ki yashar Adonai, tzuri v'lo avlata bo.

MIKOLOT MAYIM

מִקֹּלוֹת מַיִם רַבִּים אַדִּירִים מִשְׁבְּרֵי יָם,
אַדִּיר בַּמָּרוֹם יהוה.

Mikolot mayim rabim adirim mishb'rĕ yam,
Adir bamarom Adonai.

KI HEM CHAYENU

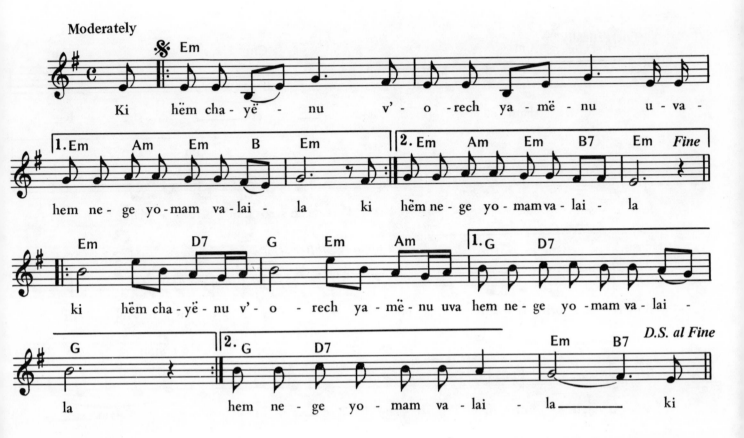

כִּי הֵם חַיֵּינוּ וְאֹרֶךְ יָמֵינוּ וּבָהֶם נֶהְגֶּה יוֹמָם וָלָיְלָה.

Ki hëm chayënu v'orech yamënu uvahem ne-ge yomam va-laila

V'SHAMRU

Continue text in similar fashion

וְשָׁמְרוּ בְנֵי יִשְׂרָאֵל אֶת־הַשַּׁבָּת, לַעֲשׂוֹת אֶת־הַשַּׁבָּת לְדֹרֹתָם
בְּרִית עוֹלָם. בֵּינִי וּבֵין בְּנֵי יִשְׂרָאֵל אוֹת הִיא לְעֹלָם

V'shamru v'në Yisraël et hashabat, la-asot et hashabat l'dorotam
b'rit olam. Bëni uven b'në Yisraël ot hi l'olam

VAY'CHULU

Based on L. Lewandowski

Recitative ad lib.

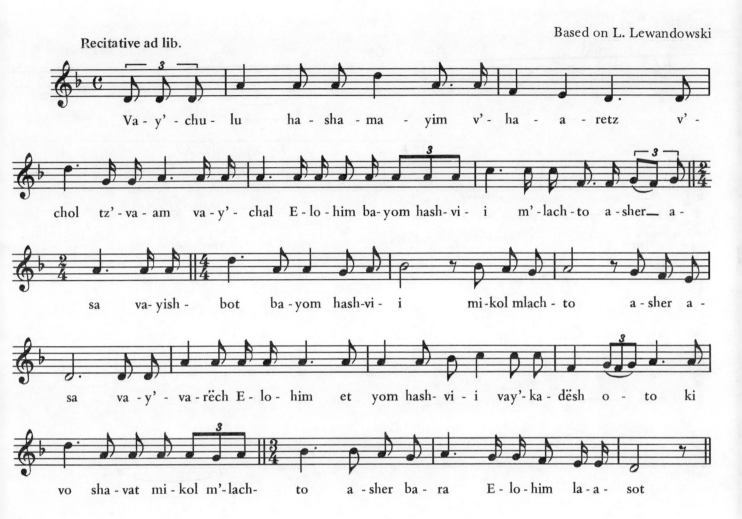

Va - y' - chu - lu ha - sha - ma - yim v' - ha - a - retz v' -
chol tz' - va - am va - y' - chal E - lo - him ba - yom hash - vi - i m' - lach - to a - sher a -
sa va - yish - bot ba - yom hash - vi - i mi - kol mlach - to a - sher a -
sa va - y' - va - rëch E - lo - him et yom hash - vi - i vay' - ka - dësh o - to ki
vo sha - vat mi - kol m' - lach - to a - sher ba - ra E - lo - him la - a - sot

וַיְכֻלּוּ הַשָּׁמַיִם וְהָאָרֶץ וְכָל־צְבָאָם: וַיְכַל אֱלֹהִים בַּיּוֹם הַשְּׁבִיעִי
מְלַאכְתּוֹ אֲשֶׁר עָשָׂה וַיִּשְׁבֹּת בַּיּוֹם הַשְּׁבִיעִי מִכָּל־מְלַאכְתּוֹ
אֲשֶׁר עָשָׂה: וַיְבָרֶךְ אֱלֹהִים אֶת־יוֹם הַשְּׁבִיעִי וַיְקַדֵּשׁ אֹתוֹ כִּי בוֹ
שָׁבַת מִכָּל־מְלַאכְתּוֹ אֲשֶׁר־בָּרָא אֱלֹהִים לַעֲשׂוֹת:

Vay'chulu hashamayim v'ha-aretz v'chol tz'va-am: Vay'chal Elohim bayom hashvi-i
M'lachto asher asa vayishbot bayom hashvi-i mikol m'lachto asher asa. Vay'varëch
Elohim et yom hash-vi-i vay'kadësh oto, ki vo shavat mikol m'lachto asher bara
Elohim la-a-sot.

KEL HAHODA'OT

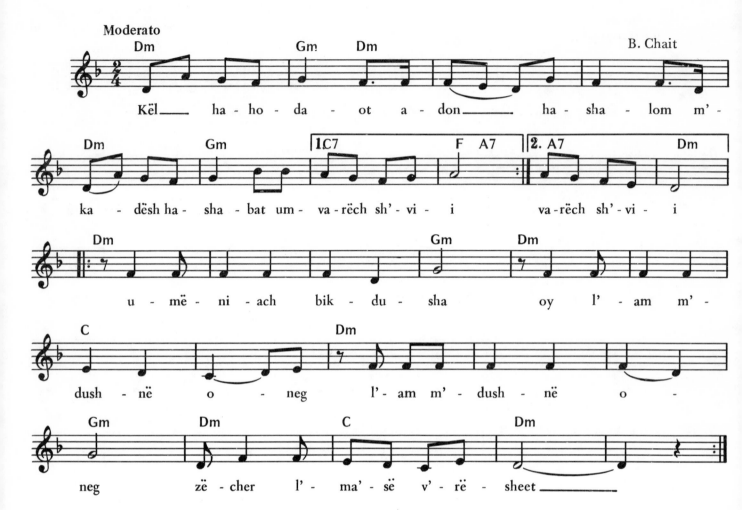

אֵל הַהוֹדָאוֹת, אֲדוֹן הַשָּׁלוֹם, מְקַדֵּשׁ הַשַּׁבָּת וּמְבָרֵךְ
שְׁבִיעִי. וּמֵנִיחַ בִּקְדֻשָׁה לְעַם מְדֻשְׁנֵי־עֹנֶג, זֵכֶר
לְמַעֲשֵׂה בְרֵאשִׁית.

Kël ha-hoda-ot adon hashalom m'kadësh hashabat um'varëch
Sh'vi-i. Umëni-ach bikdusha l'am m'dushnë oneg, zëcher
L'ma-a-së v'rë-sheet.

MI HA'ISH

מִי הָאִישׁ הֶחָפֵץ חַיִּים, אֹהֵב יָמִים לִרְאוֹת טוֹב.

נְצֹר לְשׁוֹנְךָ מֵרָע וּשְׂפָתֶיךָ מִדַּבֵּר מִרְמָה.

סוּר מֵרָע וַעֲשֵׂה טוֹב, בַּקֵּשׁ שָׁלוֹם וְרָדְפֵהוּ.

Mi ha-ish he-chafëtz chayim, ohëv yamim lirot tov.
N'tzor l'shoncha më-ra usfatecha midabër mirma.
Sur më-ra va-asë tov, bakësh shalom v'rodfëhu.

SHIRU LO

S. Mendelowitz

In march time

שִׁירוּ לוֹ שִׁיר חָדָשׁ,
הֵיטִיבוּ נַגֵּן בִּתְרוּעָה.
כִּי יָשָׁר דְּבַר יהוה,
וְכָל־מַעֲשֵׂהוּ בֶּאֱמוּנָה.

Shiru lo shir chadash
Hëtivu nagën bitru-a
Ki yashar d'var Ḥashem
V'chol ma-a-sëhu be-e-muna

EN AROCH

אֵין עֲרוֹךְ לְךָ יהוה וְאֵין זוּלָתֶךָ, אֶפֶס בִּלְתֶּךָ, וּמִי דוֹמֶה לָךְ. אֵין עֲרוֹךְ לְךָ, בָּעוֹלָם הַזֶּה, וְאֵין זוּלָתְךָ לָעוֹלָם הַבָּא. אֶפֶס בִּלְתְּךָ לִימוֹת הַמָּשִׁיחַ, וְאֵין דּוֹמֶה לְךָ לִתְחִיַּת הַמֵּתִים.

Ën aroch l'cha Hashem v'ën zulatecha efes biltecha
Umi do-me lach. En aroch l'cha ba-olam ha-ze v'ën
zulat'cha la-olam ha-ba efes bil-t'cha limot ha-ma-shi-ach
V'ën do-me l'cha lit-chi-at hamëtim.

Text as found in the Nusach S'phard prayerbook

V'ENENU

In easy fashion

Based on a Yiddish folksong

וְעֵינֵינוּ תִרְאֶינָה מַלְכוּתֶךָ, כַּדָּבָר הָאָמוּר בְּשִׁירֵי עֻזֶךָ,
עַל יְדֵי דָוִד מְשִׁיחַ צִדְקֶךָ.

V'ënënu tirena malchutecha, kadavar ha-a-mur b'shirë uzecha,
Al y'dë David m'shiach tzidkecha.

70

YISMACH MOSHE

Allegro moderato

Yis - mach yis -mach Mo - she b' - mat - nat chel - ko

ki e -ved ne - e -man ki e -ved ne' -man ka - ra - ta lo k' -

lil tif - e -ret b' - ro -sho na -ta - ta b' -

am -do l' -fa - ne -cha al har si - nai ush' -në lu -chot a -

va -nim ho -rid b' -ya - do v' -cha -tuv ba -hem shmi -rat

Sha -bat v' -chën ka -tuv b' -to -ra -te - cha

וִישְׂמַח מֹשֶׁה בְּמַתְּנַת חֶלְקוֹ, כִּי עֶבֶד נֶאֱמָן קָרֵאתָ לּוֹ. כְּלִיל
תִּפְאֶרֶת בְּרֹאשׁוֹ נָתַתָּ, בְּעָמְדוֹ לְפָנֶיךָ עַל הַר סִינַי. וּשְׁנֵי
לוּחוֹת אֲבָנִים הוֹרִיד בְּיָדוֹ, וְכָתוּב בָּהֶם שְׁמִירַת שַׁבָּת, וְכֵן
כָּתוּב בְּתוֹרָתֶךָ:

Yismach Moshe b'matnat chelko, ki eved ne-eman karata lo. K'lil
Tiferet b'rosho natata, b'amdo l'fanecha al har sinai. Ushnë
Luchot avanim horid b'yado, v'chatuv bahem sh'mirat Shabat, v'chën
Katuv b'toratecha:

YISM'CHU

Joyously

Em

Yis - m'-chu___ yis - m'-chu___ v'- mal - chut-cha sho-m'-rë___

Am ... Em ... Em ... Am

Sha - bat v'-ko-rë o - neg am m'- ka-d'-shë m'-

Em ... Am ... D7 ... G

ka-d'-shë sh'- vi - i ku - lam yis - b'- u___

G ... Em

v'- yit - an - gu___ mi - tu - ve - cha u - vash - vi - i

Am ... Em ... D7 ... G

ra - tzi - ta bo___ v'- ki - dash - to___

Em ... Am ... C ... D ... Em

chem - dat___ ya - mim___ o - to ka - ra - ta___ zë (2) cher

1. Em ... G ... 2. G ... B7 ... Em

zë - cher l'- ma - a - së v'- rë - sheet l'ma-a-së v'- rë - sheet

יִשְׂמְחוּ בְמַלְכוּתְךָ שׁוֹמְרֵי שַׁבָּת וְקוֹרְאֵי עֹנֶג. עַם מְקַדְּשֵׁי
שְׁבִיעִי, כֻּלָּם יִשְׂבְּעוּ וְיִתְעַנְּגוּ מִטּוּבֶךָ. וּבַשְּׁבִיעִי רָצִיתָ בּוֹ
וְקִדַּשְׁתּוֹ, חֶמְדַּת יָמִים אוֹתוֹ קָרָאתָ, זֵכֶר לְמַעֲשֵׂה בְרֵאשִׁית.

Yism'chu v'malchutcha shom-rë Shabat v'kor-ë oneg. Am m'kadshë
Sh'vi-i, kulam yis-b'u v'yitangu mituvecha. Uvash-vi-i ratzita bo
V'kidashto, chemdat yamim oto karata, zëcher l'ma-a-së v'rë-sheet.

V'TAHER LIBENU

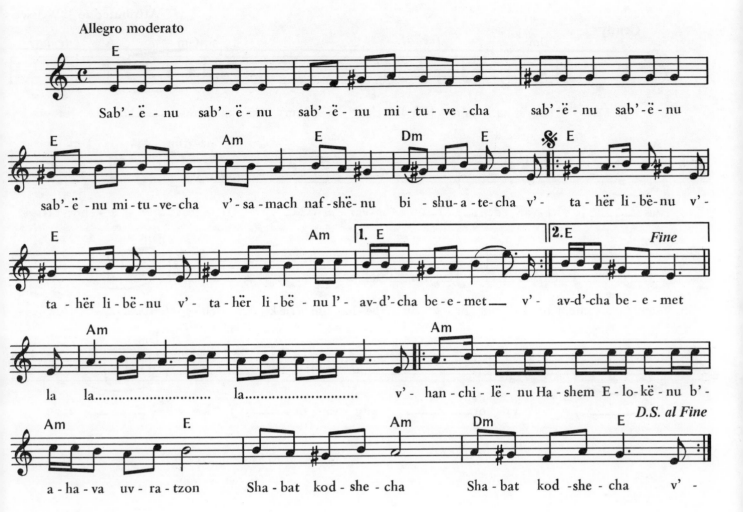

שַׁבְּעֵנוּ מִטּוּבֶךָ וְשַׂמְּחֵנוּ בִּישׁוּעָתֶךָ, וְטַהֵר לִבֵּנוּ *
לְעָבְדְּךָ בֶּאֱמֶת. וְהַנְחִילֵנוּ יהוה אֱלֹהֵינוּ בְּאַהֲבָה
וּבְרָצוֹן שַׁבַּת קָדְשֶׁךָ,

Sab'ënu mituvecha v'samach nafshënu bi-shu-a-techa
V'tahër libënu l'av-d'cha be-e-met. V'han-chi-lenu
Adonai Elohenu b'ahava uvratzon Shabbat kodshe-cha.

Text as found in the Nusach S'phard prayerbook

MA L'CHA HAYAM

Attributed to J. Weisser

מַה לְּךָ הַיָּם כִּי תָנוּס, הַיַּרְדֵּן תִּסֹּב לְאָחוֹר.
הֶהָרִים תִּרְקְדוּ כְאֵילִים, גְּבָעוֹת כִּבְנֵי־צֹאן.

Ma l'cha hayam ki tanus, hayardën tisov l'achor.
Heharim tirk'du ch'ëlim g'va-ot kiv-në tzon.

YISRAEL B'TACH BASHEM

S. Carlebach

יִשְׂרָאֵל בְּטַח בַּיהוה, עֶזְרָם וּמָגִנָּם הוּא.

Yisraël b'tach Bashem, ezram uma-ginam hu.

Y'VARECH

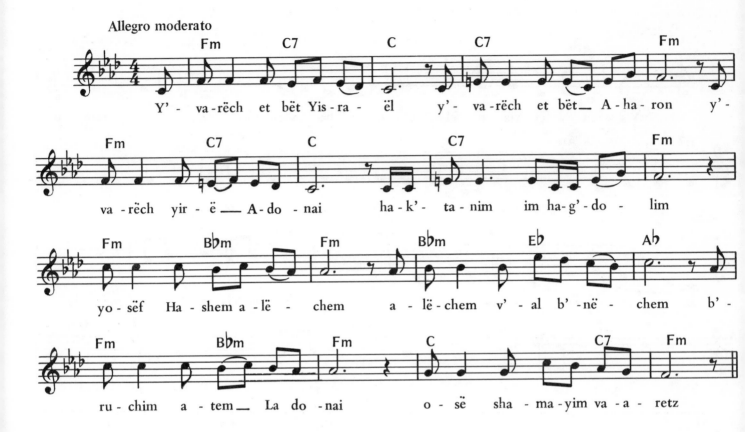

יְבָרֵךְ אֶת־בֵּית יִשְׂרָאֵל,
יְבָרֵךְ אֶת־בֵּית אַהֲרֹן.
יְבָרֵךְ יִרְאֵי יהוה, הַקְּטַנִּים עִם הַגְּדֹלִים.
יֹסֵף יהוה עֲלֵיכֶם, עֲלֵיכֶם וְעַל בְּנֵיכֶם.
בְּרוּכִים אַתֶּם לַיהוה, עֹשֵׂה שָׁמַיִם וָאָרֶץ.

Y'varëch et bet Yisraël
Y'varëch et bët Aharon.
Y'varëch yir-ë Hashem, hak'tanim im hag'dolim.
Yosëf Adonai alëchem, alëchem v'al b'nëchem.
B'ruchim Ladonai, o-së shamayim va-a-retz.

HAL'LU

הַלְלוּ אֶת־יהוה כָּל־גּוֹיִם, שַׁבְּחוּהוּ כָּל־הָאֻמִּים.
כִּי גָבַר עָלֵינוּ חַסְדּוֹ, וֶאֱמֶת יהוה לְעוֹלָם. הַלְלוּיָהּ.

Hal'lu et Hashem kol goyim, shab'chuhu kol ha-umim
Ki gavar alënu chasdo, ve-emet Hashem l'olam. Hal'luya.

HODU

הוֹדוּ לַיהוה כִּי טוֹב, כִּי לְעוֹלָם חַסְדּוֹ.
יֹאמַר נָא יִשְׂרָאֵל, כִּי לְעוֹלָם חַסְדּוֹ.

Hodu Ladonai ki tov, ki l'olam chasdo.
Yomar na Yisraël, ki l'olam chasdo.

MIN HAMETZAR

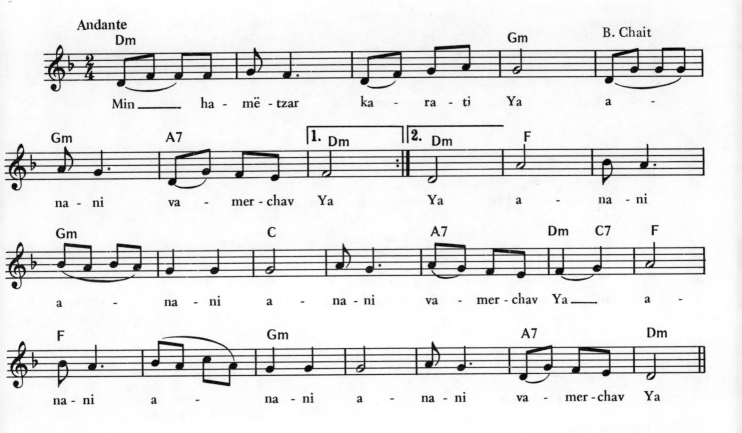

מִן הַמֵּצַר קָרָאתִי יָהּ, עֲנָנִי בַמֶּרְחָב יָהּ.

Min hamëtzar karati Ya, anani vamerchav ya.

KOL RINA

קוֹל רִנָּה וִישׁוּעָה בְּאָהֳלֵי צַדִּיקִים,
יְמִין יהוה עֹשָׂה חָיִל.

Kol rina vi-shu-a b'o-ho-lĕ tzadikim
Y'min Hashem o-sa chayil.

PITCHU LI

פִּתְחוּ לִי שַׁעֲרֵי צֶדֶק, אָבֹא בָם, אוֹדֶה יָהּ.
זֶה הַשַּׁעַר לַיהוה, צַדִּיקִים יָבֹאוּ בוֹ.

Pitchu li sha-a-rë tzedek avo vam, o-de Ya.
Ze hasha-ar Lashem, tzadikim ya-vo-u vo.

82

OD'CHA

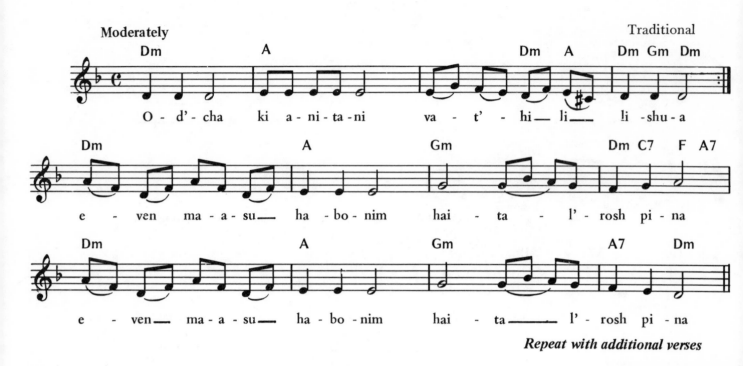

Moderately   Traditional

O - d' - cha   ki   a - ni - ta - ni   va - t' - hi - li — li - shu - a

e - ven   ma - a - su —   ha - bo - nim   hai - ta - l' - rosh   pi - na

e - ven — ma - a - su —   ha - bo - nim   hai - ta — l' - rosh   pi - na

Repeat with additional verses

אוֹדְךָ כִּי עֲנִיתָנִי וַתְּהִי לִי לִישׁוּעָה.
אֶבֶן מָאֲסוּ הַבּוֹנִים הָיְתָה לְרֹאשׁ פִּנָּה.

**Od'cha ki anitani vat'hi lishu-a.
Even ma-a-su habonim hai-ta l'rosh pina.**

KELI ATA

Hassidic

Slowly with devotion

Kë - li a - ta v' - o - de - ka E - lo - kai a - ro - m' - me - ka

Kë - li a - ta v' - o - de - ka E - lo - kai a - ro - m' - me - ka

Kë - li a - ta v' - o - de - ka E - lo - kai a - ro - m' - me - ka

Kë - li a - ta v' - o - de - ka E - lo - kai a - ro - m' - me - ka

אֵלִי אַתָּה וְאוֹדֶךָּ, אֱלֹהַי אֲרוֹמְמֶךָּ.

Këli ata v'odeka Elokai arom'meka

AV HARACHAMIM

אָב הָרַחֲמִים, הֵיטִיבָה בִרְצוֹנְךָ אֶת־צִיּוֹן, תִּבְנֶה חוֹמוֹת יְרוּשָׁלָיִם.
כִּי בְךָ לְבַד בָּטַחְנוּ, מֶלֶךְ אֵל רָם וְנִשָּׂא, אֲדוֹן עוֹלָמִים.

Av harachamim, hëtiva vir-tzoncha et Tziyon, tivne chomot Y'rushalayim.
Ki v'cha l'vad batachnu, melech Ël ram v'nisa, adon olamim.

KI MITZIYON

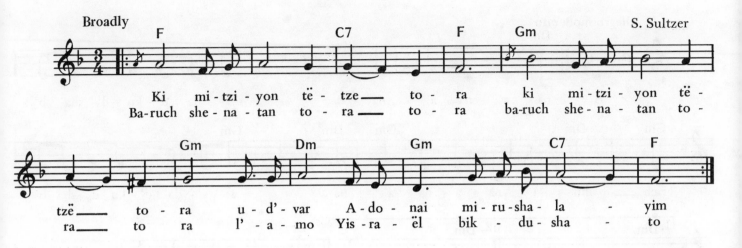

Broadly   S. Sultzer

Ki mi-tzi-yon të-tze to-ra ki mi-tzi-yon të-
Ba-ruch she-na-tan to-ra to-ra ba-ruch she-na-tan to-

tzë to-ra u-d'-var A-do-nai mi-ru-sha-la-yim
ra to ra l'-a-mo Yis-ra-ël bik-du-sha-to

כִּי מִצִּיּוֹן תֵּצֵא תוֹרָה, וּדְבַר יהוה מִירוּשָׁלָיִם.
בָּרוּךְ שֶׁנָּתַן תּוֹרָה לְעַמּוֹ יִשְׂרָאֵל בִּקְדֻשָׁתוֹ.

Ki Mitziyon tëtzë Tora, ud'var Adonai Mirushalayim.
Baruch she-natan Tora l'amo Yisraël bik-du-shato.

ANA AVDA

אֲנָא עַבְדָּא דְקֻדְשָׁא בְּרִיךְ הוּא.

Ana avda d'kud'sha b'rich hu

BE ANA RACHITZ

Traditional
Attributed to Z. Rovner

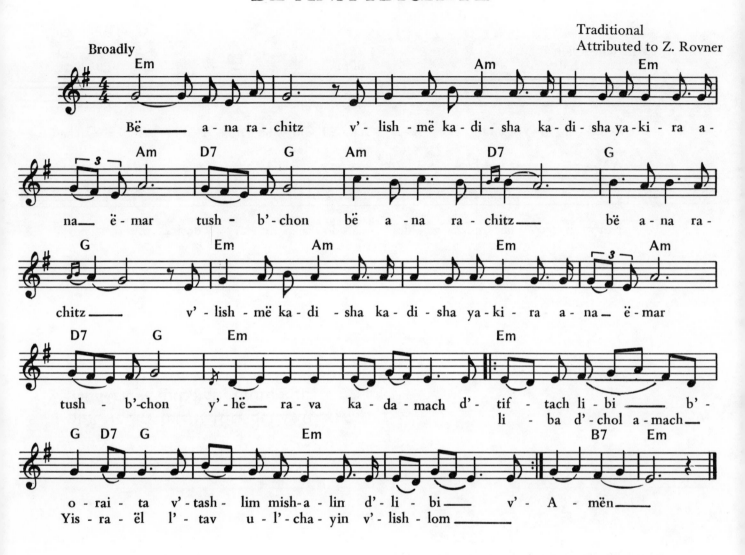

בֵּהּ אֲנָא רָחִיץ וְלִשְׁמֵהּ קַדִּישָׁא
יַקִּירָא אֲנָא אֵמַר תֻּשְׁבְּחָן. יְהֵא רַעֲוָא קֳדָמָךְ דְּתִפְתַּח לִבִּי
בְּאוֹרַיְתָא, וְתַשְׁלִים מִשְׁאֲלִין דְּלִבִּי וְלִבָּא דְכָל־עַמָּךְ יִשְׂרָאֵל,
לְטָב וּלְחַיִּין וְלִשְׁלָם. אָמֵן.

Bë ana rachitz v'lishmë kadisha
Yakira ana ëmar tush-b'chan. Y'hë ra-a-va ko-damach d'tiftach li-bi
B'o-rai-ta, v'tashlim mish-a-lin d'libi v'liba d'chol amach Yisraël,
L'tav ul'chayin v'lishlam. Amën.

SH'MA YISRAEL

Traditional

Sh' - ma Yis - ra - ël A - do - nai E - lo - hë - nu A - do - nai e - chad

E - chad E - lo - hë - nu ga - dol a - do - në - nu ka - dosh____ sh' - mo

שְׁמַע יִשְׂרָאֵל יהוה אֱלֹהֵינוּ יהוה אֶחָד.
אֶחָד אֱלֹהֵינוּ, גָּדוֹל אֲדוֹנֵינוּ, קָדוֹשׁ (וְנוֹרָא) שְׁמוֹ.

Sh'ma Yisraël Adonai Elohënu Adonai Echad.
Echad Elohënu, gadol Adonënu, Kadosh (v'nora) sh'mo.

VA-ANI T'FILATI

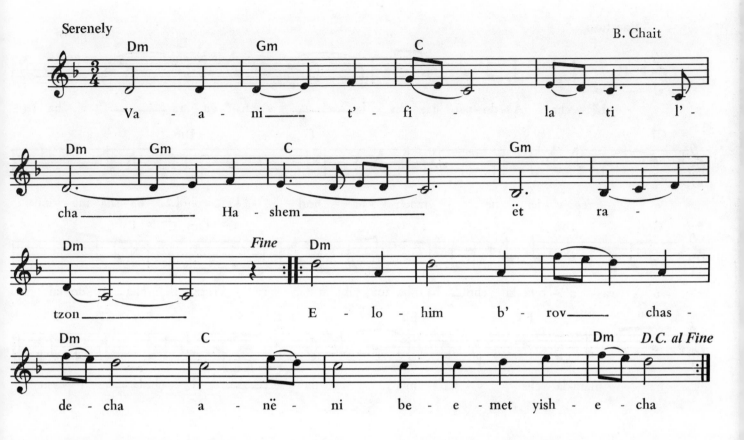

וַאֲנִי תְפִלָּתִי לְךָ יהוה עֵת רָצוֹן, אֱלֹהִים בְּרָב חַסְדֶּךָ עֲנֵנִי
בֶּאֱמֶת יִשְׁעֶךָ.

Va-ani t'filati l'cha Hashem ët ratzon, Elohim b'rov chasdecha a-nëni
B'emet yish-e-cha.

L'CHA ADONAI

לְךָ יהוה הַגְּדֻלָה וְהַגְּבוּרָה וְהַתִּפְאֶרֶת וְהַנֵּצַח וְהַהוֹד, כִּי כֹל
בַּשָּׁמַיִם וּבָאָרֶץ, לְךָ יהוה הַמַּמְלָכָה וְהַמִּתְנַשֵּׂא לְכֹל לְרֹאשׁ.

L'cha Adonai hagdula v'hagvura v'hatiferet v'hanëtzach v'hahod, ki chol
Bashamayim uva-aretz, l'cha Adonai hamamlacha v'hamitna-së l'chol l'rosh.

ZARA CHAYA

זַרְעָא חַיָּא וְקַיָּמָא, זַרְעָא דִּי לָא יִפְסַק
וְדִי לָא יִבְטַל מִפִּתְגָּמֵי אוֹרַיְתָא

Zara chaya v'kayama, zara di la yifsuk
V'di la yivtul mipit-ga-më o-rai-ta

BIRCHAT HACHODESH

יְהִי רָצוֹן מִלְפָנֶיךָ יהוה אֱלֹהֵינוּ וֵאלֹהֵי אֲבוֹתֵינוּ, שֶׁתְּחַדֵּשׁ
עָלֵינוּ אֶת־הַחֹדֶשׁ הַזֶּה לְטוֹבָה וְלִבְרָכָה. וְתִתֶּן לָנוּ חַיִּים
אֲרֻכִּים, חַיִּים שֶׁל שָׁלוֹם, חַיִּים שֶׁל טוֹבָה, חַיִּים שֶׁל בְּרָכָה,
חַיִּים שֶׁל פַּרְנָסָה, חַיִּים שֶׁל חִלּוּץ עֲצָמוֹת, חַיִּים שֶׁיֵּשׁ בָּהֶם
יִרְאַת שָׁמַיִם וְיִרְאַת חֵטְא, חַיִּים שֶׁאֵין בָּהֶם בּוּשָׁה וּכְלִמָּה,
חַיִּים שֶׁל עֹשֶׁר וְכָבוֹד, חַיִּים שֶׁתְּהֵא בָנוּ אַהֲבַת תּוֹרָה וְיִרְאַת
שָׁמַיִם, חַיִּים שֶׁיִּמָּלְאוּ מִשְׁאֲלוֹת לִבֵּנוּ לְטוֹבָה, אָמֵן סֶלָה.

*This text has been adapted to the tune of
Keli Ata. See page 83.*

Y'hi ratzon milfanecha Adonai Elohḯnu velohḯ avotḯnu, she-t'chadḯsh
Alḯnu et hachodesh ha-ze l'tova v'livracha. V'titen lanu chayim arukim,
Chayim shel shalom, chayim shel tova, chayim shel b'racha, chayim shel
Parnasa, chayim shel chilutz atzamot, chayim sheyḯsh bahem yirat shamayim
V'yirat chḯt, chayim she-ḯn bahem busha uch-lima, chayim shel osher v'chavod,
Chayim shet'hḯ vanu ahavat tora v'yirat shamayim, chayim she-y'mal'u mishalot
Libḯnu l'tova, Amḯn sela.

MI SHE-ASA NISIM

Mi ____ she-a-sa ____ ni-sim ____ la-a-vo-të-nu v'-ga-al ____ o-tam ____ më-av-dut l'-chë-rut hu yig-al o-ta-nu b'-ka-rov vi-ka-bëtz ni-da-chë-nu më-ar-ba kan-fot ha-a-retz cha-vë-rim ____ kol ___ Yis-ra-ël v'-no-mar a-mën

מִי שֶׁעָשָׂה נִסִּים לַאֲבוֹתֵינוּ וְגָאַל אוֹתָם מֵעַבְדוּת לְחֵרוּת, הוּא
יִגְאַל אוֹתָנוּ בְּקָרוֹב וִיקַבֵּץ נִדָּחֵינוּ מֵאַרְבַּע כַּנְפוֹת הָאָרֶץ,
חֲבֵרִים כָּל-יִשְׂרָאֵל, וְנֹאמַר אָמֵן.

Mi she-asa nisim la-avotënu v'ga-al otam më-avdut l'chërut, hu
Yigal otanu b'karov vikabëtz nidachënu më-arba kanfot ha-aretz,
Chavërim kol Yisraël, v'nomar amën.

Y'CHADSHEHU

יְחַדְּשֵׁהוּ הַקָּדוֹשׁ בָּרוּךְ הוּא עָלֵינוּ וְעַל כָּל־עַמּוֹ בֵּית יִשְׂרָאֵל
לְחַיִּים וּלְשָׁלוֹם, לְשָׂשׂוֹן וּלְשִׂמְחָה, לִישׁוּעָה וּלְנֶחָמָה, וְנֹאמַר
אָמֵן.

Y'chadshëhu hakadosh baruch hu alënu v'al kol amo bët Yisraël
L'chayim ul'shalom, l'sason ul'simcha. lishu-a ul'nechama, v'nomar
Amën.

HODO AL ERETZ

Maestoso

Traditional

Ho - do al e - retz v'-sha - ma - yim va - ya - rem — ke - ren l'-

a — mo t'- hi — la l'- chol cha - si - dav

liv - në Yis - ra - ël___ am k'ro - vo Ha - l'- lu — ya

הוֹדוֹ עַל אֶרֶץ וְשָׁמַיִם, וַיָּרֶם קֶרֶן לְעַמּוֹ
תְּהִלָּה לְכָל־חֲסִידָיו, לִבְנֵי יִשְׂרָאֵל עַם קְרֹבוֹ. הַלְלוּיָהּ.

Hodo al eretz v'shamayim, vayarem keren l'amo
T'hila l'chol chasidav, liv-në Yisraël am k'rovo. Hal'luya.

ETZ CHAYIM HI

עֵץ חַיִּים הִיא לַמַּחֲזִיקִים בָּהּ, וְתוֹמְכֶיהָ מְאֻשָּׁר.
דְּרָכֶיהָ דַרְכֵי־נֹעַם, וְכָל־נְתִיבוֹתֶיהָ שָׁלוֹם.
הֲשִׁיבֵנוּ יהוה אֵלֶיךָ וְנָשׁוּבָה, חַדֵּשׁ יָמֵינוּ כְּקֶדֶם.

Etz chayim hi lamachazikim ba, v'tomcheha m'ushar.
D'racheha darchë no-am, v'chol n'tivoteha shalom.
Hashivënu Adonai ëlecha v'nashuva, chadësh yamënu k'kedem.

ETZ CHAYIM HI No.2

T. Portnoy

shu - va k' - ke - dem _____

עֵץ חַיִּים הִיא לַמַּחֲזִיקִים בָּהּ, וְתוֹמְכֶיהָ מְאֻשָּׁר.
דְּרָכֶיהָ דַרְכֵי-נֹעַם, וְכָל-נְתִיבוֹתֶיהָ שָׁלוֹם.
הֲשִׁיבֵנוּ יהוה אֵלֶיךָ וְנָשׁוּבָה, חַדֵּשׁ יָמֵינוּ כְּקֶדֶם.

Ëtz chayim hi lamachazikim ba, v'tomcheha m'ushar.
D'racheha darchë no-am, v'chol n'tivoteha shalom.
Hashivënu Adonai ëlecha v'nashuva, chadësh yamënu k'kedem.

NA-ARITZCHA

Na-aritzcha v'nakdishcha k'sod si-ach sarfё kodesh hamakdishim shimcha
Bakodesh, kakatuv al yad n'vi-echa, v'kara ze el ze v'amar:

נַעֲרִיצְךָ וְנַקְדִּישְׁךָ כְּסוֹד שִׂיחַ שַׂרְפֵי קֹדֶשׁ הַמַּקְדִּישִׁים שִׁמְךָ
בַּקֹּדֶשׁ, כַּכָּתוּב עַל יַד נְבִיאֶךָ, וְקָרָא זֶה אֶל זֶה וְאָמַר:

K'VODO

With movement

K' - vo - do___ ma - lë___ o - lam m' - shar - tav sho - a - lim ze la -

ze k' - vo - do ma - lë___ o - lam m' -

shar - tav sho - a - lim ze la - ze a - yë a - yë

a - yë a - yë a - yë m' - kom k' - vo - do

a - yë a - yë a - yë a - yë a - yë m' - kom k' - vo - do

כְּבוֹדוֹ מָלֵא עוֹלָם, מְשָׁרְתָיו שׁוֹאֲלִים זֶה לָזֶה: אַיֵּה מְקוֹם כְּבוֹדוֹ.

K'vodo ma-lë olam, m'shartav sho-alim ze la-ze: a-yë m'kom k'vodo.

MIMKOMO

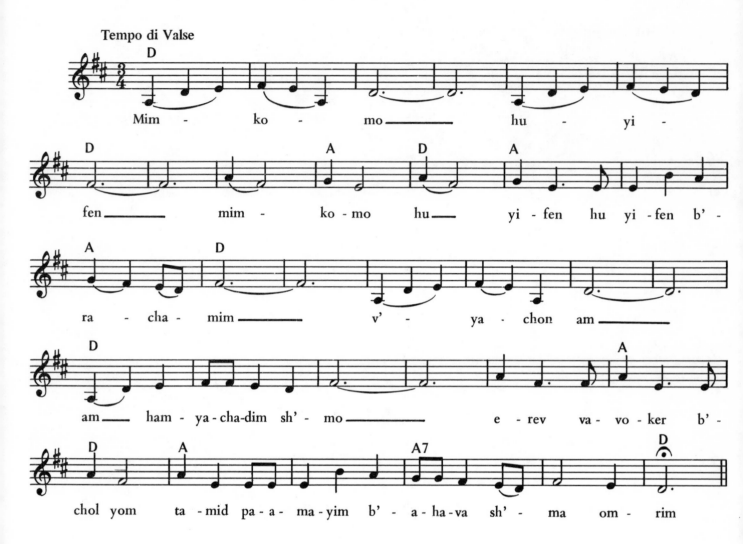

Tempo di Valse

Mim - ko - mo _____ hu - yi -

fen _____ mim - ko - mo hu _____ yi - fen hu yi - fen b' -

ra - cha - mim _____ v' - ya - chon am _____

am _____ ham - ya - cha - dim sh' - mo _____ e - rev va - vo - ker b' -

chol yom ta - mid pa - a - ma - yim b' - a - ha - va sh' - ma om - rim

מִמְּקוֹמוֹ הוּא יִפֶן בְּרַחֲמִים, וְיָחוֹן עַם הַמְיַחֲדִים שְׁמוֹ עֶרֶב
נָבְקֶר בְּכָל-יוֹם תָּמִיד פַּעֲמַיִם בְּאַהֲבָה שְׁמַע אוֹמְרִים:

Mimkomo hu yifen b'rachamim, v'yachon am ham'yachadim sh'mo
Erev vavoker b'chol yom tamid pa-a-mayim b'ahava sh'ma omrim:

SH'MA YISRAEL

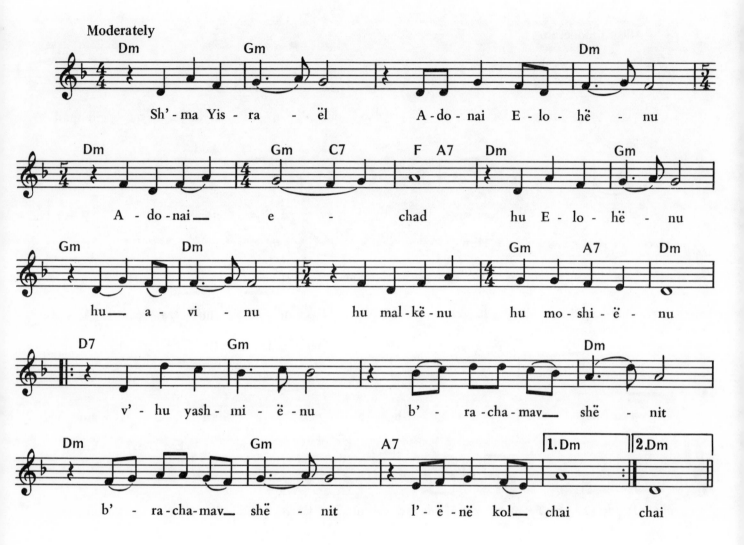

שְׁמַע יִשְׂרָאֵל יהוה אֱלֹהֵינוּ יהוה אֶחָד.

הוּא אֱלֹהֵינוּ, הוּא אָבִינוּ, הוּא מַלְכֵּנוּ, הוּא מוֹשִׁיעֵנוּ, וְהוּא
יַשְׁמִיעֵנוּ בְּרַחֲמָיו שֵׁנִית לְעֵינֵי כָּל־חָי

Sh'ma Yisraël Adonai Elohënu Adonai echad.

Hu Elohënu, hu Avinu, hu Malkënu, hu Moshi-ënu,
V'hu yash-mi-ënu b'rachamav shënit l'ënë kol chai.

L'DOR VADOR

Allegro moderato

S. Zim

L' - dor va - dor l' - dor va - dor l' - dor va - dor na - gid god -

le - cha___ l' - dor va - dor l' - dor va - dor l' - dor va -

dor na - gid god - le - cha___ u - l' - në - tzach n' - tza - chim k' - du -

shat - cha nak - dish k' - du - shat - cha nak - dish___ v' - shiv - cha -

cha E - lo - hë - nu mi - pi - nu lo ya - mush l' - o - lam l' - o - lam va - ed

לְדוֹר וָדוֹר נַגִּיד גָּדְלֶךָ וּלְנֵצַח נְצָחִים קְדֻשָּׁתְךָ נַקְדִּישׁ. וְשִׁבְחֲךָ
אֱלֹהֵינוּ מִפִּינוּ לֹא יָמוּשׁ לְעוֹלָם וָעֶד

L'dor vador nagid god-le-cha ul'nëtzach n'tza-chim k'dushatcha nakdish,
V'shiv-cha-cah Elohënu mi-pinu lo yamush l'olam va-ed.

UV'YOM HASHABAT

Adapted from
M. Machtenberg

וּבְיוֹם הַשַּׁבָּת, שְׁנֵי כְבָשִׂים בְּנֵי שָׁנָה תְּמִימִם, וּשְׁנֵי עֶשְׂרֹנִים סֹלֶת
מִנְחָה בְּלוּלָה בַשֶּׁמֶן וְנִסְכּוֹ. עֹלַת שַׁבָּת בְּשַׁבַּתּוֹ עַל עֹלַת הַתָּמִיד
וְנִסְכָּהּ.

Uv'yom hashabat sh'në ch'vasim b'në shana t'mimim, ush'në esronim solet
Mincha b'lula vashemen v'nisko. Olat Shabat b'shabato al olat hatamid v'niska.

L'MA-AN ACHAI

S. Carlebach

L'-ma-an a-chai v'-rë-ai ____ l'-ma-an a-chai v'-rë-ai ____ a-dab'-ra na ____ a-dab'-ra na sha-lom ____ bach ____ l'-bach ____ l'-ma-an bët ____ Ha-shem E-lo-kë-nu a-vak-sha tov ____ lach ____ l'-ma-an bët ____ Ha-shem E-lo-kë-nu a-vak-sha tov ____ lach ____ l'-lach ____

לְמַעַן אַחַי וְרֵעָי, אֲדַבְּרָה-נָּא שָׁלוֹם בָּךְ. לְמַעַן בֵּית יהוה
אֱלֹהֵינוּ, אֲבַקְשָׁה טוֹב לָךְ.

L'ma-an achai v'rë-ai, adabra na shalom bach. L'ma-an bët Hashem
Elokënu avaksha tov lach.

ATA ECHAD

Ata echad v'shimcha echad, umi k'amcha Yisraël goy echad ba-aretz.
Tiferet g'dula va-a-teret y'shu-a, yom m'nucha ukdusha l'amcha natata
Avraham yagël Yitzchak y'ranën, Ya-akov uvanav yanuchu vo.

B'NE VETCHA

בְּנֵה בֵיתְךָ כְּבַתְּחִלָּה וְכוֹנֵן מִקְדָּשְׁךָ עַל מְכוֹנוֹ, וְהַרְאֵנוּ
בְּבִנְיָנוֹ וְשַׂמְּחֵנוּ בְּתִקוּנוֹ

B'në vëtcha k'vatchila v'chonën mikdashcha al m'chono, v'harënu
B'vinyano v'samchënu b'tikuno

MA'OZ TZUR

Traditional

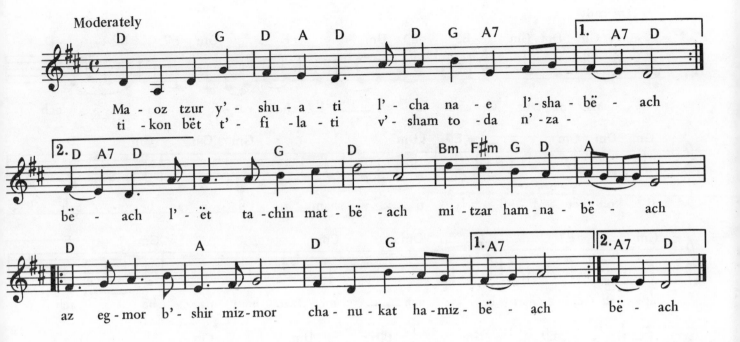

Ma - oz tzur y'- shu - a - ti   l'- cha na - e   l' - sha - bë - ach
ti - kon bët t' - fi - la - ti   v'- sham to - da   n' - za -

bë - ach   l' - ët   ta - chin mat - bë - ach   mi - tzar ham - na - bë - ach

az   eg - mor   b' - shir miz - mor   cha - nu - kat ha - miz - bë - ach   bë - ach

מָעוֹז צוּר יְשׁוּעָתִי לְךָ נָאֶה לְשַׁבֵּחַ.
תִּכּוֹן בֵּית תְּפִלָּתִי וְשָׁם תּוֹדָה נְזַבֵּחַ.
לְעֵת תָּכִין מַטְבֵּחַ מִצָּר הַמְנַבֵּחַ.
אָז אֶגְמוֹר בְּשִׁיר מִזְמוֹר חֲנֻכַּת הַמִּזְבֵּחַ.

Ma-oz tzur y'shu-ati l'cha na-e l'sha-bë-ach
Tikon bët t'filati v'sham toda n'za-bë-ach
L'ët tachin mat-bë-ach mitzar ham-na-bë-ach
Az egmor b'shir mizmor cha-nu-kat hamiz-bë-ach.

MA'OZ TZUR No.2

B. Marcello

מָעוֹז צוּר יְשׁוּעָתִי לְךָ נָאֶה לְשַׁבֵּחַ.
תִּכּוֹן בֵּית תְּפִלָּתִי וְשָׁם תּוֹדָה נְזַבֵּחַ.
לְעֵת תָּכִין מַטְבֵּחַ מִצָּר הַמְנַבֵּחַ.
אָז אֶגְמוֹר בְּשִׁיר מִזְמוֹר חֲנֻכַּת הַמִּזְבֵּחַ.

Ma-oz tzur y'shu-ati l'cha na-e l'sha-bë-ach.
Tikon bët t'filati v'sham toda n'za-bë-ach.
L'ët tachin mat-bë-ach mitzar ham-na-bë-ach
Az egmor b'shir mizmor cha-nu-kat hamizbë-ach.

Y'VANIM

Y'vanim nikb'tzu alai azai bi-më chashmanim
Ufartzu chomot migdalai v'timu kol hashmanim
Uminotar kankanim na-asa nës lashoshanim
B'në vina y'më shmona kavu shir ur'nanim.

אָזַי בִּימֵי חַשְׁמַנִּים,
וְטִמְּאוּ כָּל הַשְׁמָנִים,
נַעֲשָׂה נֵס לַשׁוֹשַׁנִּים,
קָבְעוּ שִׁיר וּרְנָנִים.

יְוָנִים נִקְבְּצוּ עָלַי
וּפָרְצוּ חוֹמוֹת מִגְדָּלַי
וּמִנּוֹתַר קַנְקַנִּים
בְּנֵי בִינָה יְמֵי שְׁמוֹנָה